Mommy, Do I *Have* To Serve A Mission?

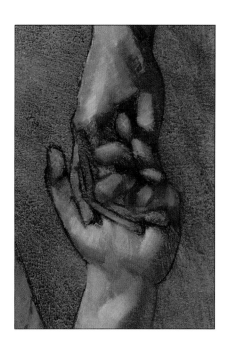

TOKEN Ink

Once there was a little boy who loved his mommy. He loved the rest of his family too, but he really loved his mommy. Now this little boy was a Mormon, and one day he learned that little Mormon boys grow up to be big Mormon missionaries.

"Mommy, do I *have* to serve a mission?" he asked.

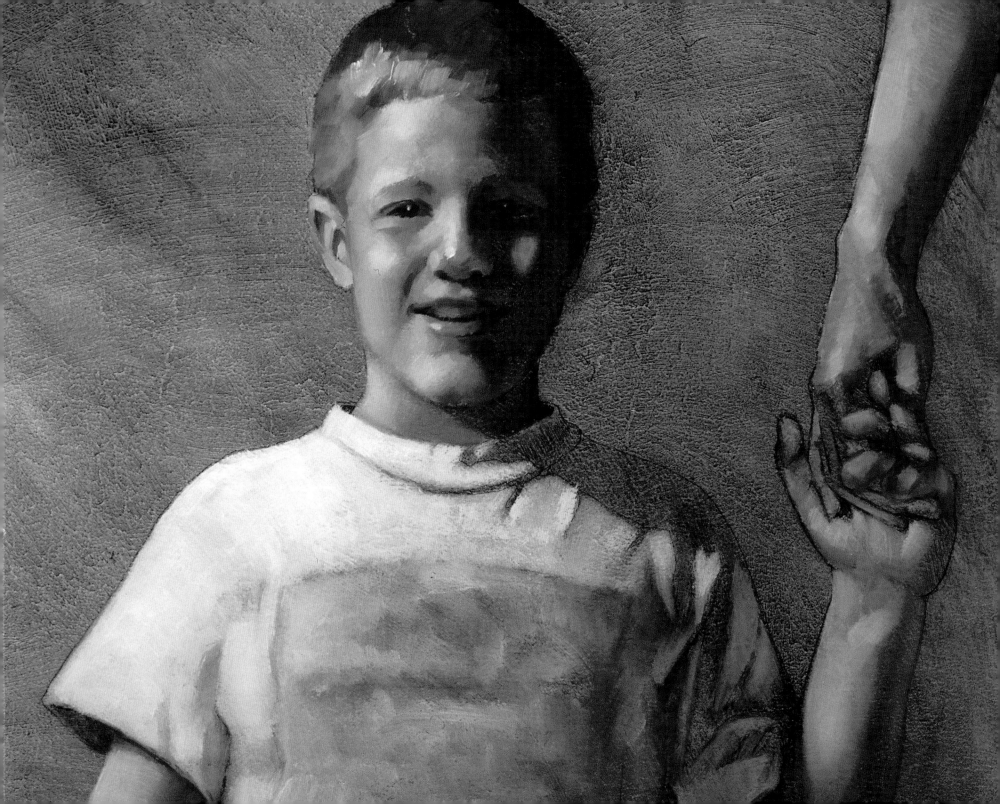

She smiled and knelt down so that they were the very same height. He liked it when she did that because their noses matched exactly—well, almost.

The mother thought long and hard about what she should say, and how she should say it. "When you grow up, I believe that you will want to serve a mission. You will want to teach people about Heavenly Father and Jesus and the Plan of Salvation."

"But I love the people here. This is my home. This is where I belong."

His mother wrapped her arms all the way around him and held him tight, like she would never let go.

"What's wrong, son?" she asked.

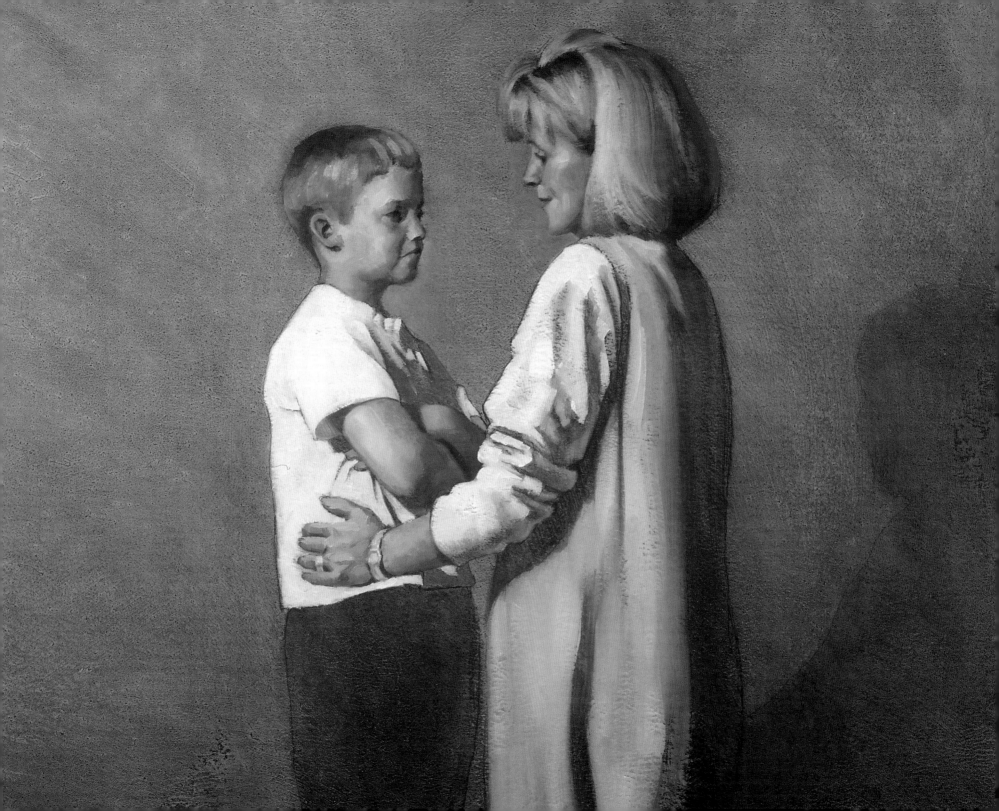

His little lip quivered like JELL-O™ salad at Sunday dinner. Hot tears filled his eyes and boiled down his cheeks. "I will miss you, Mommy. Will you miss me?"

"Oh, yes, son. I will miss you."

"Will you write me letters all the time, and put my letters on the fridge just like you do my pictures of dragons?"

"Sure, I will," she promised. Then she looked into his brave young eyes and said, "I will miss you, son, so much it will hurt. But it will be a happy hurt."

He wasn't sure about that, so he stared at his mother for a long time. "Okay," he finally said, "but I can't swim."

Now it was her turn to stare in wonder. "You don't have to swim on your mission."

"But won't I have to go to the Empty Sea first?"

She grinned. "You mean The MTC."

"That's what I said, not the Full Sea."

When the boy turned eight years old he read *The Book of Mormon*—not all by himself; his family helped him and sometimes, his mother played special tapes while they were driving.

She taught him about Jesus, and about heroes like Ammon, and Alma and Samuel and lots of different Nephis.

Then he got all dressed in white and was baptized and confirmed.

"You are following in the footsteps of Jesus, taking on his holy name," his bishop told him. "I believe that one day you'll choose to be a great missionary."

The boy smiled, then frowned, and searched for his mother.

"What's wrong, son?" she asked in a low voice.

His lip quivered like JELL-O™ salad at Sunday dinner. He wiped his nose with his shirt sleeve. "I'm scared," he replied. "I *want* to follow Jesus, but what if I make mistakes?"

"Oh, you will," she promised. "We all do. But I will love you, no matter what. And Heavenly Father and Jesus will always be just a prayer away. You will never be alone, son."

The boy stepped back and thought. "I *want* to be a missionary, Mommy, but it's a lot of work, isn't it?"

"Yes," said the mother, "being a missionary is a lot of hard work."

She gave him an extra squeeze, brushed the hair out of his eyes, and kissed his forehead.

He sniffled and asked, "Do *you* think I'll be a great missionary, Mommy?"

She smiled and bent over so that they were the same height and their noses matched exactly—well, almost. "Yes, son."

His face swung from side to side. He wanted to make sure no one else was looking. "But I will miss you, Mommy. Will you miss me?"

His mother drew a deep breath. "Oh, yes, son. I will miss you."

He dragged his shirt sleeve across his face again. "But I love the people here. This is my home. This is where I belong."

That mother wrapped her arms all the way around her son and held him tight, like she would never let go.

When he backed away, he questioned, "You can't go with me on my mission, can you, Mommy?"

She shook her head, "No, son."

"Will you take lots of pictures of me and put them all over the house so that you won't forget how handsome I am?"

"Sure, I will," she promised. Then she looked into his eyes and repeated, "I will miss you, son, so much it will hurt. But it will be a happy hurt."

He brushed the hair back down over his eyes. "I love you, Mommy," he whispered, so that only she could hear.

• • •

That young boy grew into a young man with long arms and extra long legs. Some nights he read parts of *The Book of Mormon.* He knelt beside his bed, prayed, then stayed on his knees, just listening. Those were good nights. Other nights, after he had been listening to too many different voices, he felt far away from the people he loved most. He wanted to tell his mother how hard it was to grow up, how much he needed her, but he didn't want her to think that he was still a little boy. So he crawled into bed telling himself that he didn't need anyone at all. Those nights weren't so good.

One day his mother took him into a special department store to buy him a new suit and a nice white shirt.

"Do I have to wear this?" he whined.

His mother leaned forward and stood on her tippy-toes so that they were the same height and their noses matched exactly—well, almost.

"What's wrong, son?"

His lip quivered like JELL-O™ salad at Sunday dinner. He turned away from her. "I look like a geek. I don't want to look like a geek."

"Yes, you do, son."

He swung back and glared at her.

She smiled. "I'm sorry. That's not what I meant. You look so handsome—just like a missionary."

His face turned to stone. "Mom, I don't *have* to serve a mission. You can't make me!"

She wrapped her arms all the way around him and held him tight, like she would never let go.

"You are right, son. It is your decision."

"I love the people here. This is my home. This is where I belong." he said.

His mother did not say another word, just kept hugging.

When the son backed away, he looked into the mirror. "Are you going to make me wear this suit to church tomorrow?"

She sighed. "I just want you to look as good on the outside as I know you are on the inside, when you bless the sacrament."

The young man took a very long time to decide. Then he looked at his mother and asked, "Does it come in blue?"

She smiled and bought the suit in blue.

Her son drove them home and on the way he asked, "*If* I go on a mission, will you give my room away while I'm gone?"

His mother tried not to smile, and had to look out the window so he would not see the hot, but happy tears, that were burning her eyes, boiling down her cheeks.

"No, son. I will not give your room away," she promised, "but I can't guarantee that it won't be invaded by the rest of the family."

. . .

All at once that young man was grown. He had read *The Book of Mormon*,

had prayed, and had decided for himself that he wanted to serve a mission.

One day he called his mother and said, "It's here."

"Where to?" she asked.

"I haven't opened it yet. I want you to be

here with me when I do."

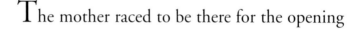

The mother raced to be there for the opening

of her son's mission call. He leaned way over so that they were the

same height and their noses matched exactly—well, almost.

She swallowed hard when she discovered that he was

going half way around the world to a place that she

had only heard of on the news.

The son wrapped his arms all the way around his mother and held her tight, like he would never let her go.

"What's wrong?" he asked.

Her lip quivered like JELL-O™ salad at Sunday dinner.

"Mom, I *have* to go on my mission," he told her.

She nodded, choking back the tears, "Yes. I know you do."

She tried not to cry at his farewell.

She tried not to cry at the airport.

She tried not to drip tears on the letters he wrote home—the letters she plastered all over the refrigerator, right next to this third grade drawing of Smoke, The Tired Dragon.

That mother wandered the house, looking at pictures of her missionary son. "I miss you," she sniffled, kneeling by the bed in his room, the room that, to her, would *always* be his.

"I thank Thee, Heavenly Father," she prayed, "please bless *our* son."

Far, far away on the other side of the world, the son stood in front of

his refrigerator—actually it was more like an icebox—and posted the latest

letter from his mother with a little magnet of Moroni, another one of his

childhood heroes.

Every time he knelt to pray, ironed his shirt, sewed on a button,

or made macaroni-and-cheese, he thought of

his *real* childhood hero…

"I miss you, Mom," he whispered to the family

photo that he kept tucked inside of his scriptures.

Two years passed, and it was time for his mission to end.

"Mom, do I have to come home?" he asked.

His mother wrote back immediately. "Yes, son. You *have* to come home."

The son came home and when his airplane landed, his mother could not wait—she

ran down the jetway to meet him. "What's wrong, son?" she asked.

His lip quivered like JELL-O™ salad at Sunday dinner. Hot tears filled his eyes and

boiled down his cheeks. "I miss them, Mom. I miss the people I learned to love there. That

became my home. That is where I belonged."

His mother wrapped her arms almost all the way around him and held him tight, like she would never let go.

"Did you miss me, Mom?" he asked.

Now she cried. She cried and cried and cried, "Oh, yes, son. I missed you. I missed you so much it hurt."

He gave her an extra tight squeeze. "I know—but it was a happy hurt, wasn't it?"

Then he lifted his mother right off the ground so that they were the same height and their noses matched exactly…

…well almost.

To

MISSIONARIES

AND TO THE MOTHERS WHO SERVE THEM!

Mommy, Do I Have To Serve A Mission?/ by Toni Sorenson Brown

Summary: A son and his mother come to understand what serving a mission for the Church of Jesus Christ of Latter-day Saints entails.
ISBN 1-889354-01-5
[1. Church of Jesus Christ of Latter-day Saints—fiction. 2. Mothers and Sons—fiction. 3. Mormon Missionaries—fiction.]
This book is not an official publication of the Church of Jesus Christ of Latter-day Saints.

Models provided by the Bryan and Natalie Burr family

Printed in China by Palace Press
First TOKEN Ink printing August 2000